A Present for Charlie

by Dawn McMillan
illustrated by Susy Boyer

Harcourt
SCHOOL PUBLISHERS

Printed in Mexico

ISBN 10: 0-15-351415-9
ISBN 13: 978-0-15-351415-9

Ordering Options
ISBN 10: 0-15-351212-1 (Grade 2 Advanced Collection)
ISBN 13: 978-0-15-351212-4 (Grade 2 Advanced Collection)
ISBN 10: 0-15-358050-X (package of 5)
ISBN 13: 978-0-15-358050-5 (package of 5)

1 2 3 4 5 6 7 8 9 10   050   15 14 13 12 11 10 09 08 07 06

Grandpa had photographs from
all over the world, but there was one
photograph in his album that the boys
liked best.

3

"Is that really Grandpa?" Craig asked in amazement. "He's so young!"

"It's Grandpa, all right," said Charlie, "and he's riding a go-cart. I wish I had a go-cart!"

4

That night, Craig thought about a present for Charlie. His birthday was on the next Saturday. Craig couldn't buy him a go-cart, but he did have great idea for a present.

5

The next day, Craig found Grandpa working in the shed.

"Grandpa," he said, "I wonder if you could help me make Charlie a go-cart for his birthday. I know I've seen some wheels in this shed."

"Oh, yes!" said Grandpa. "I had lots of fun on my go-cart when I was your age."

"If we make Charlie a go-cart, how will we keep it a secret?" Craig asked.

"We'll make it here, in the back room of the shed," said Grandpa. "He'll never know what we are up to."

Grandpa found the wheels Craig
had seen, and then he and Craig sorted
out the wood that they needed. They
gathered some tools, and Craig found
a can of bright red paint.

All week, Grandpa and Craig worked
together to make the go-cart. If Craig
saw Charlie coming, he would quickly
shut the door of the shed.

10

When the go-cart was finished,
Craig got down on one knee and
painted it a bright fire-engine red.

"It looks like a million dollars!"
laughed Grandpa. "When the paint is
dry, we'll attach the steering rope."

On the morning of Charlie's birthday, Grandpa helped Craig bring the go-cart up the drive to the garden gate.

"Happy birthday, Charlie!" shouted Craig.

"Wow!" exclaimed Charlie with surprise. "It's a go-cart!"

Charlie put on his helmet and rode the go-cart down around the curve of the drive.

"It's wonderful!" he puffed, as he pulled it back up the hill again. "Come on, Craig! Let's ride together!"

Dad rode the go-cart, and Mom, and then Grandpa wanted a turn.

"Whee!" squealed Grandpa as he went around the curve.

He didn't look so different from that boy in the picture from many years ago.

14

Think Critically

1. Why did Craig decide to make a go-cart for Charlie?

2. How did Grandpa help Craig keep the go-cart a surprise?

3. What did Grandpa mean when he said the go-cart looked "like a million dollars"?

4. What did you predict would happen when Grandpa rode in the go-cart?

5. What toy would you like to try and make? Why?

 Social Studies

Then and Now Paragraph Write a paragraph telling how things children do for fun today are different from things children did for fun long ago.

School-Home Connection Tell a family member what Craig did for Charlie in the story. Talk about a time when someone gave you nice surprise.